D1506148

The Hunter I Might Have Been

The Hunter I Might Have Been

by George Mendoza

photographed by
De Wayne Dalrymple

ASTOR-HONOR, INC.

For John Ledes . . .

And if the soul
is to know itself
it must look
into a soul:
the stranger and enemy, we've seen him in the mirror.

From: *ARGONAUTS*
COLLECTED POEMS, 1924-1955
by George Seferis
Trans. ed. by E. Keeley & P. Sherrard
© Princeton University Press 1967.

When I was a boy, barely tall,

I shot a sparrow from a tree

I held its limp body in my hands

and buried it still warm in the soft earth

Then I fled.

I never touched a gun again.

But years came later when I was a man

I wondered,

oh, the hunter I might have been

had I but met a lion that first day

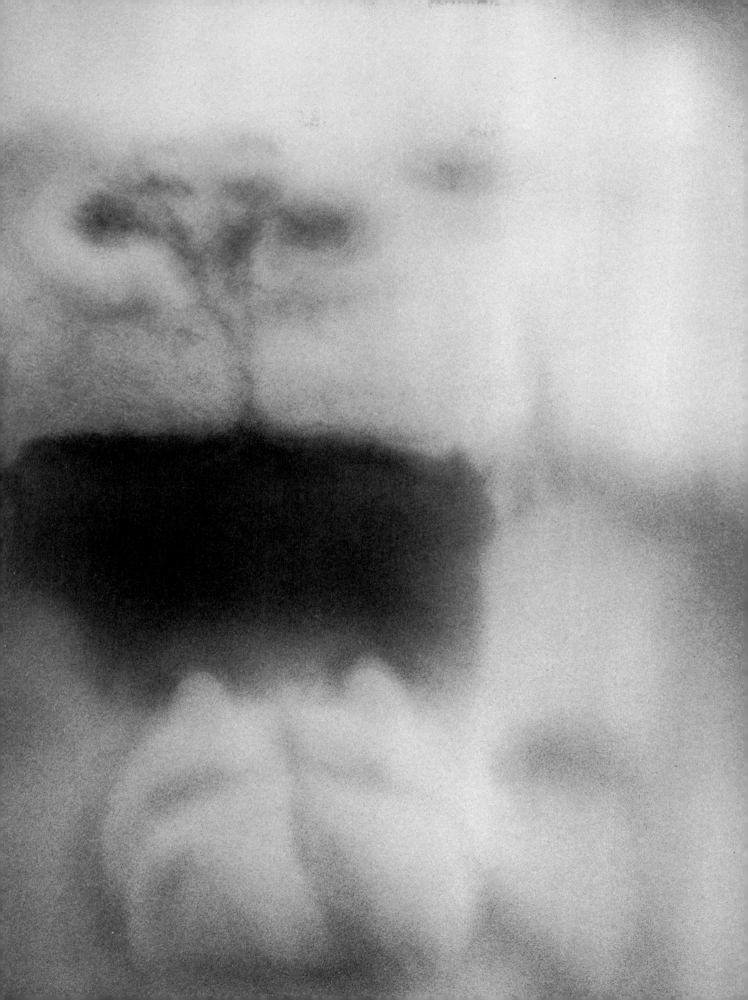

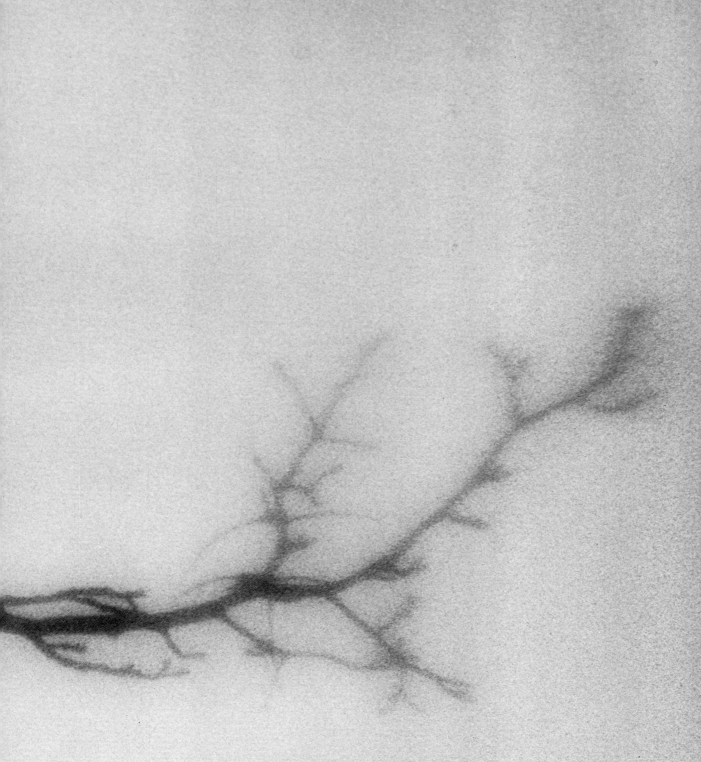

and not stilled that gentle sparrow's call.